# LITTLE TEI
# First Six Weeks

BURP!

Charlotte Preston, RHV, RGN    Trevor Dunton

**For Alfie, Sophie, Tilly, Theo, Emilio and Sofia**

First published in Great Britain in 1998 by Metro Books
(an imprint of Metro Publishing Limited), 19 Gerrard Street, London W1V 7LA

All rights reserved: no part of this publication may be reproduced, stored in a retrieval system,
or transmitted in any form or by any means, electronic, mechanical, photocopying or
otherwise, without the prior written consent of the publisher.

Text © 1998 Charlotte Preston and Trevor Dunton
Illustrations © 1998 Trevor Dunton

Charlotte Preston and Trevor Dunton are hereby identified as the authors of this work in
accordance with Section 77 of the Copyright, Designs and Patents Act 1988.

British Library Cataloguing in Publication Data.
A CIP record of this book is available on request from the British Library.

ISBN 1 900512 22 X

10  9  8  7  6  5  4  3  2  1

Designed by Mick Keates
Typesetting and formatting by Concise Artisans
Printed in Italy by LEGO

*An extra bit for parents with girls*
*You'll find that throughout the Little Terror books we refer to babies as 'he'.*
*Please don't think we've neglected your daughters, it's purely in the interests of clarity and*
*space. Using he/she, him/her, himself/herself is cumbersome to read and uses valuable space*
*that we wanted to devote to more useful topics. So, please read 'she' for 'he'.*

# CONTENTS

# DON'T PANIC!

This book is about helping you to survive Little Terror's first six weeks. Like many soon-to-be parents you've probably spent the last nine months in count-down mode, preparing for the big day. You may have conscientiously attended all the classes and read all the books until you were totally clued up on the three stages of labour, could recognise a contraction and had breathing pretty well sussed. However, birth is such a momentous, daunting and wonderful event in itself that it's easy to forget what happens on the other side.

Then, suddenly, there you are on your doorstep proudly holding your own very real Little Terror in your arms, and wondering how on earth you are going to cope. DON'T PANIC!

Before you know it, you'll be the world's leading expert on that warm bundle you're holding. This book is designed to give you a bit of a head start and, if nothing else, to reassure you that you're doing just fine.

We have broken the first six weeks down into the following topics:

- 🎀 Coming home
- 🎀 Feeding – breast or formula?
- 🎀 The crying game – wind and sleep
- 🎀 Washing and bathing
- 🎀 Nappies
- 🎀 Taking LT out
- 🎀 Health and safety

# COMING HOME

*Never the same again*

If you had a hospital birth, bringing your new baby home is very special. It's probably at this point that it begins to dawn on you that life will never be the same again. Wonderful – yes, exhausting – definitely. You won't have time for anything apart from caring for

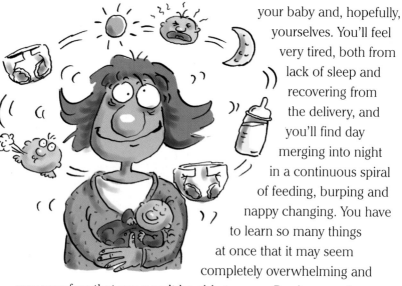

your baby and, hopefully, yourselves. You'll feel very tired, both from lack of sleep and recovering from the delivery, and you'll find day merging into night in a continuous spiral of feeding, burping and nappy changing. You have to learn so many things at once that it may seem completely overwhelming and you may fear that you won't be able to cope. Don't worry, in a few weeks it really does get better. It's also important to realise that before you know it you'll be looking back fondly at this time when everything was new and you and LT were just getting to know each other. Try to enjoy it!

Unlike sleep, one thing you definitely won't be short of is advice.

Everyone, from the local greengrocer to Mrs Knowitall at no. 57, thinks they're a childcare expert. Follow your own instincts. Remember that this Little Terror is *your* baby and then do what is right for *you*.

9

## Mood swings and depression

For a new mum, the first few weeks can be an emotional roller-coaster. If you feel blissfully happy one minute then despairing and tearful the next, you could have the 'Baby Blues'. It's easy to underestimate how exhausted you are and, on top of this, your hormones are going through a period of change. If you're feeling fragile, be kind to yourself. You'll start levelling out at around six weeks.

If the feeling doesn't improve, or even gets worse, you may be suffering from post-natal depression. If you don't seem to be feeling better, and are perhaps having problems bonding with LT, it's very important to share your worries straight away. Let your partner, or a close friend, know how awful you feel. Their support might be enough to get you through. In any case, talk to your health visitor, who will give you support and also information on specialist help in your area. Your GP might prescribe medication and refer you to a counsellor. With help you are likely to make a full recovery.

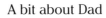

## A bit about Dad

Becoming a father is a strange and wondrous time. You'll feel yourself pulled all over the place by a bucketload of unfamiliar emotions. You may have been through the birth at your partner's side, seen your baby born, held him or her in your arms, then suddenly you're back home wondering what hit you. When she comes home, your partner, who used to be quite reasonable, is having Jekyll-and-Hyde-type mood swings, you can't seem to do a thing right and every conversation is about nappies, wind or colic! What are you supposed to be doing, anyway?

If you're feeling left out, even jealous, remember that you can make a big difference to LT's first six weeks. First, by supporting and helping your partner as much as you can, and then, by getting stuck in yourself! LT is your baby too, and you need to get to know each other. It won't take long before one of those special Little Terror smiles gets you right there, and it might just surprise you to find that you can settle your wailing LT even better than Mum.

Not to mention the serious satisfaction a pretty slick piece of nappy changing can bring.

*Polish up your nappy-changing techniques*

## Bonding

Bonding is nature's way of ensuring that you put up with your
Little Terror when he is causing you some serious grief, and that
you continue to do so throughout his childhood and beyond.
Many mothers feel very attached to their babies before or straight
after birth, but don't worry if you don't. It can take a couple of
weeks, or even longer.

## Sex and contraception

Discuss how you feel with your partner. You're quite likely to be
more interested in sleep at this stage. If you're still very sore, sex is
probably the last thing on your mind, but it is safe to make love as
soon as you both feel ready (this might be before your six-week check
or after several months). Note: You will need contraception. Don't
assume you're safe while you are still breastfeeding, or before your
periods begin again, unless you want Little Terror II on your hands.

*You might be
more interested in
sleep for a while*

# SURVIVAL TIPS

🎀 GET HELP! Drag in trusted friends and relations, even if they just baby-sit for half an hour or rustle up a meal while you have a nap or a bath. You owe yourself a break and you will feel all the more loving towards LT afterwards. If you are all right, he will be all right too.

🎀 Doctors and health visitors are there to help. If you're worried, don't hesitate to contact them. You'll probably be in touch with the medical services more in LT's first year than for the rest of his life.

🎀 Talk to your partner. It's tough for both of you. Give each other support.

16

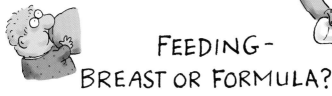

# FEEDING –
# BREAST OR FORMULA?

To help you decide whether to breast or bottle feed, here are some of the pros and cons of both. Remember it is your choice. Whichever method you decide to use, if it's right for you, it's right.

*Breastfeeding* – The good things:

🍼 It's designer-made for LT, containing everything he needs for health and development.

🍼 It's natural and easy to digest. Tummy upsets or constipation are less likely compared with bottle-fed babies.

🍼 Breast milk contains antibodies that protect LT from infections – less likelihood of illness.

🍼 He'll benefit even if you breastfeed just for the first couple of weeks.

🍼 Breast milk also seems to provide some protection against developing eczema later.

🎁 It costs you nothing, no preparation is needed and it is available 24 hours a day, sterile and at the right temperature.

🎁 If LT is premature, breast milk will give him a very special start.

🎁 LT can be bottle fed by others using your expressed breast milk.

🎁 Breastfeeding is the natural way of using up the energy stores (or fat), that are laid down during pregnancy. Or, to put it another way, breastfeeding is nature's way of slimming!

The not-so-good things:

🎁 Only LT's mum can produce the goods.

🎁 Dad can only be involved in feeding if mum has expressed her milk.

🎁 You may worry because you can't see how much he has taken.

🎁 Feeding can seem to take ages at the beginning because it takes time to get it right.

🎁 Breastfeeding can be tiring.

## *Bottle feeding with formula –*

The good things:

Dad can have a go.

It is easier to leave LT with his dad, granny, or a friend when you go out.

The feeds take less time.

It's an alternative, if you cannot bear the thought of breastfeeding.

The not-so-good things:

You will need time and energy to prepare feeds.

Formula milk costs money!

LT will be less protected from tummy upsets, infections and allergies.

19

## *Breastfeeding*

With a bit of luck, breastfeeding will work for both you and LT
from the start. But it *can* take more than three weeks to get really
established. In the early stages, your midwife is there to help you
sort out problems and get LT latched on properly so that it doesn't
hurt. After about ten days your health visitor will take over, and
support you with feeding and other aspects of baby and child care
until LT starts school at five.

*Before ...*

Successful breastfeeding depends on LT's mum being relaxed, confident and not feeling too exhausted. For the first day or two your breasts will provide a thick yellow liquid called colostrum. This has all the nutrients he needs and will protect him from infection. By offering him this as soon as you can after his birth you stimulate the hormones used

*...After*

to make milk. Breastfeeding works by supply and demand – the more LT drinks, the more milk you produce as LT's suckling causes what is called the 'let-down' reflex in your breast so that the milk flows to your nipple. In the early days, just hearing LT cry can cause the 'let-down' and your breasts might start to leak (use breast pads in your bra, and change them frequently).

## Action plan for uncomfortable breasts

Before a feed, the breasts fill up with milk and can become hard and uncomfortable; this will get better as the milk starts to flow. If your breasts become uncomfortable:

🎀 Take immediate action and try expressing a little milk before each feed. This can also help avoid mastitis (inflamed or blocked milk ducts).

🎀 Take a hot shower or bath. This can help the flow.

🎀 If your breasts are hot and painful, try putting cold compresses of frozen peas (seriously!) or (even stranger) cabbage leaves inside your bra. Some people swear by it!

🎀 Paracetamol tablets can help you through the first few days.

🎀 Don't stop breastfeeding or offer a bottle.

## Tips for establishing problem-free breastfeeding

🎀 Feed LT frequently, letting him stay on one breast for as long as he wants, then offering him the other. Remember to change breasts next feed. The watery fore-milk is more for quenching his thirst and the rich hind-milk makes him grow. Don't give bottles at night, as night breastfeeds help to build up your milk supply.

🎀 Even if things aren't going too well, it's worth persevering. Remember that you are giving him something very special and, once you have stopped, you can't start again.

🎀 Let him feed on demand. Don't clock-watch or take him off the breast before he has finished. If he has six wet nappies and is gaining weight, he is getting enough milk. Don't expect a feeding routine for the first four to six weeks.

🎀 As LT's mum, you need to look after yourself so that you can provide all that lovely breast milk. Dad can help by bringing you a cup of tea and making sure you have a snack (new mothers often say that they don't have time to eat). You will need a lot of support and encouragement while breastfeeding is getting established.

## Getting comfortable

The right position is very important for breastfeeding. Sit holding him very close with his head and body facing you, or lie on your side with LT lying alongside with his nose in line with your nipple. Wait until his mouth is wide open and bring him to your breast (not vice versa) so that he can take in your nipple and the area around it, with more of the breast from below the nipple. Don't hold him away from you so that he pulls on your breast, but let him rest his head in the crook of your arm.

When he is latched on, make sure his chin is against your breast and his lower lip turned out. Let LT take the nipple, don't push it into his mouth, as his tongue will move against the nipple instead of the breast, causing sore nipples. Once in position, LT will suck deeply for most of the feed and come off when he has had enough. It's normal for him to stop and start a bit, pulling his head away from time to time.

Let him have his fill of the first breast, then wind him if you want to and offer the second breast. If he has had enough after one breast, remember to offer the other breast first at the next feed. It won't take long to work out what is best for you and LT.

*Dad can help by bringing you a snack*

25

## Bottle feeding with formula

Formula milk is cow's milk that has been specially modified to be as much like mother's milk as possible. Just to confuse you, there are lots of different brands. Make sure you start with one labelled 'first' as some are for older babies and will be harder for LT to digest.

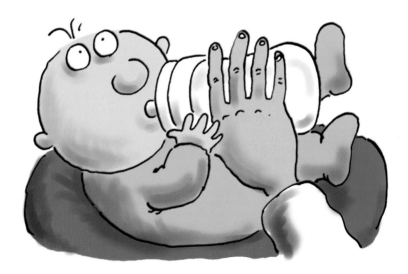

Feeding is a time to get close to LT. It's important to be comfortable, relaxed and unhurried. Get as much support as you can. You will need both help and rest to achieve this.

## Washing and sterilising

To wash your bottles and teats, use washing-up liquid in water, squirting it through the teats and using a bottle brush for the bottles. Make sure you get rid of any trace of milk, because old milk harbours germs and LT isespecially vulnerable during the first few weeks.

There are several different ways to sterilise bottles and teats. You can use chemical sterilising

*Old milk harbours germs*

tablets or liquid, which you make up into a solution and put into a plastic container with a lid. Put the washed bottles and teats in the container and check there are no air bubbles. This can be purchased as a kit.

Steam sterilisers are quick and efficient and there are also special microwave bottle sterilisers.

Before chemicals and gadgets, mums used to boil the bottles in a saucepan for five minutes to kill the germs. This method can be used for emergencies.

### Getting prepared

Before you bring LT home you will need six bottles and teats. With many different types and sizes, you'll need to experiment to get the teat that flows at the right rate for LT. Make sure you have supplies of formula milk and sterilising equipment for the first few days.

28

## Tips for successful bottle feeding

Always wash your hands before making up feeds. To start with, LT will probably feed little and often. Feed him on demand. As long as his weight is OK, let him decide how much he wants. There's no need to force food down him. If he's crying, it's not necessarily because he's hungry (see the following section on crying).

The manufacturers give a rough guide to the number and size of feeds your baby will need, but this will vary, as all babies are different. Never add extra scoops (which can cause dehydration) or use less formula as he won't get enough nourishment. Most babies, whether breast or bottle fed, lose weight in the first few days, but usually return to their birth weight by two to three weeks old.

If LT is bottle fed regularly, offer him cooled, boiled water between feeds, as he may get thirsty.

## Making up feeds

Boil the water and pour the correct amount into the bottle. Let it cool, then measure the formula with the scoop and add it to the bottle. Shake thoroughly. You can make up several bottles at a time. Keep prepared feeds in the fridge for up to 24 hours. Throw away unused milk each time. Don't use bottled water as it might contain the wrong salts.

Teats that are too small can cause LT to suck too hard so he will get tired and take in wind. Similarly, if they are too large, LT will gulp and splutter, get frustrated and, again, take in wind. Change the teat if it blocks. If a teat flattens while feeding, gently pull on the bottle to release the vacuum.

*Check that the milk isn't coming out too fast . . .*

## Mixing breast and bottle feeding

This is another option once breastfeeding is well established. There might be several reasons for going down this path:

You may be a reluctant breastfeeder and about to give up altogether. If this is the case, it's still better for LT to have some breast milk than none at all.

You might be very tired and absolutely desperate for a rest.

You might be returning to work and want to gradually introduce a bottle.

*... or too slow*

# THE CRYING GAME -
# WIND AND SLEEP

If Little Terror's first cry is music to your ears, it isn't necessarily a
tune that improves the more times you hear it. If, during serious
bouts of wailing, you find your inner smile wearing a bit thin,
remember that all over the world thousands of other parents are
going through the same thing.

Crying is normal. All babies do it, some more, some less, and for a variety of different reasons. You may find that your Little Terror is just more sensitive to his surroundings than other babies and more easily disturbed. Remember that you can only do your best. Get as much practical help as you can from close friends or relatives, even if they just take LT for a walk to the shops, look after yourselves and try to catch up on lost sleep. Good luck.

At the end of this section there's a checklist on causes of crying, with an action plan, which you can use for quick reference.

## *All about crying*

Without much of a vocabulary, crying is the only way Little Terror can communicate. He'll let you know when he's hungry, thirsty, windy or sleepy, when he doesn't want a bath or would have preferred it if you'd left his nappy off, thanks. He might just be a bit fed up, or object to being put down to sleep. You'll discover lots of reasons why your Little Terror cries and all of them are normal. You will soon learn to distinguish between a sudden scream: I could be in pain, immediate response please; and a fretting cry: it might be worth leaving me for a few minutes to see if I'll settle on my own.

For the first three months, babies are not able to cry at will. However, after this time, if LT carries on crying for long periods it could be that he has learnt that you will always respond.

No one really knows why, but babies all over the world cry most in the evening. If your baby cries a lot, it's easy to feel inadequate. Remember there is no evidence that normal crying harms babies. It has nothing to do with *your* experience. It's a lottery. It's not your fault.

How much crying is normal?

You may have a Little Treasure from the start, who cries very little, or a Little Terror who cries for three hours a day. Both are normal. Average crying time is about two hours in twenty-four. Even if it seems to you that he is crying all the time, your LT is probably no worse than any other, but you suffer every second of it. If he really won't stop, and you are worried, seek medical advice.

Crying time usually peaks at six weeks and then halves by about three months. This is because colic (which is related to digestive problems and causes tummy pain) and wind get better at about this time.

Why is he crying?

Use this checklist for quick reference to help you decide why your baby's crying and what action to take.

# CHECK LIST

1. Hungry? Feed on demand.

2. Nappy full? Change.

3. Wind? Help him burp. See page 39.

4. Too hot or cold? What are you wearing? He will need a little more on than you.

5. Tired? Calm him down with a walk or a drive. Put him in a sling or his cot.

*Nappy full?*

**6** Wants a cuddle? Give him lots.

**7** Wants to suck? It's OK to use a dummy.

**8** Upset with his milk? Check your diet if breastfeeding; if bottle-feeding, check type and strength of formula.

**9** Constipated? Extra water, then very diluted orange or prune juice.

**10** Unwell? Check there is nothing seriously wrong. If he is ill, seek advice immediately.

**11** Life too hectic? Slow down.

**12** Screaming in bath? Afterwards, try calming him with a baby massage.

38

## Wind

Wind is caused by LT gulping milk and swallowing a lot of air with it. This gets trapped and causes pain. The cure for wind is burping. However, Britain is the only part of Europe where babies are winded after every feed – so bear in mind you might be fussing over LT unnecessarily. Hold him upright against your shoulder or support him sitting up, and pat or rub his back to help him burp. He might bring up some milk as you are winding him. They call it possetting, but you'll probably call it being sick down your neck.

If LT has colic, it's painful and he'll scream the place down, draw his legs up and hopefully pass some serious gas! Colic is caused by his immature intestine going into spasm and making bubbles of air, which have to come out of one end or the other. The bad news is: it's very upsetting. The good news is: it gets better by about three months.

40

## Sleep

When Mrs Knowitall tells you her baby slept for twenty-nine hours a day, don't believe a word of it! New babies are generally awake for about eight hours a day, and sleep for varying amounts of time at a stretch. Unreasonably, LT won't fit in with your sleep routine, so you need to sneak in a nap whenever you can.

It's worth introducing good sleeping habits right from the start, so try getting LT to go to sleep on his own once a day. Instead of nursing or cuddling him to sleep, rock him in his crib or push him in his pram. Pat him or sing to him. Many new parents don't realise that it's OK to put LT down awake. Note: on his back.

# WASHING AND BATHING

It's quite normal for first-time parents to feel completely traumatised at the thought of these mammoth tasks. After all, your baby looks so fragile and you may never have been anywhere near one before. Panic not! After the first couple of weeks, you'll probably wonder what you were so worried about.

*It's normal to feel like this*

## Washing

You don't have to bath LT every day. You can just
wash his face, neck, hands and then his bottom.
To do this you will need warm water in a
plastic bowl (use your elbow to check
that it's not too hot), a towel, cotton
wool balls, nappy cream (optional)
and a clean nappy and clothes. Make
sure the room
is nice and warm
and choose a time
when he is happy and not hungry
(though not just after a feed).

1 Hold LT on your knee or put him on
a changing mat, strip him down to his
vest and nappy, then wrap him up in
a towel.

43

2 Dip the cotton wool ball in the water, squeeze out the excess and wipe around the eyes from the nose outwards, using a separate ball for each eye to prevent cross-infection. Use a fresh ball for each ear, but don't clean inside as you don't want infection to get into the inner ear.

3 In the same way, wash the rest of his face and neck, being sure to get into his creases. Now do his hands. Dry him gently with the towel as you go.

4 LT's cord will shrivel and drop off from between a week to ten days. Wipe his navel with a wet cotton wool ball, using cooled, boiled tap-water.

5 Remove the nappy and see what you've got! If his nappy is dirty, clean him with tissue or wipes to get the worst off, then finish off with baby soap (optional) and wet cotton wool balls. You should not pull back your baby boy's foreskin.

6 Dry him with a towel and let him have a kick without his nappy on. If any other areas are mucky, wash them in the same way. You can then put a barrier cream on the whole area, if you like, to prevent nappy rash. Don't feel a failure if LT has a sore bottom, it happens to most babies at some time. If you're doing all the right things (as above) and changing him often, and he still gets a nappy rash, show it to your health visitor or GP. It might be thrush, which will need treatment.

## Bathtime

1. Fill the baby bath or a large washing-up bowl with a few inches of water, being very careful to check the temperature. You can use baby bath liquid or soap and shampoo. Have them ready at hand.

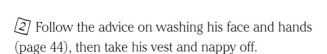

2̲ Follow the advice on washing his face and hands (page 44), then take his vest and nappy off.

3̲ Clean the nappy area, then wrap him in a towel and hold him firmly in the crook of your left arm (right, if you are left-handed), supporting his head and neck with your hand; you can then use your free hand to wash his hair with water and rinse it over the bath.

4̲ Unwrap him from the towel and put it under him, on your lap or the changing mat. Soap him all over, avoiding his face. If you use baby bath liquid, there's no need for soap.

5 Lower him into the bath holding him firmly under one of his arms and supporting his head. Use your other hand to swoosh water over him.

**6** Lift him out on to a towel on a changing mat or your knee and pat him dry, paying careful attention to those creases under his arms and around his neck. This is the perfect time to give him a gentle massage with baby or almond oil.

**7** Then put him to bed and get your partner to do the same to you (the massage bit!).

**8** When he's about six weeks and you feel confident in handling LT, how about bathing with him – most babies love having a bath with their mum or dad, though you'll probably need another pair of hands until he can sit up on his own. Important: Always check the temperature of the water before LT gets in.

# NAPPIES

One thing is certain – LT is going to fill up a lot of nappies. He won't care if they are terries or disposables, he'll fill 'em up anyway. If you want to use terries you will need to buy at least twenty-four as he will get through about twelve a day. Terries do work out cheaper than disposables but, by the time you have bought plastic pants, disposable nappy liners and nappy pins and added the cost of laundering, there is not that much in it. However, some mums and dads get quite a buzz from seeing rows of clean, white nappies blowing on the line in the sunshine.

## Keeping things clean – terries

Before washing, terries need to be soaked in a bucket of diluted sterilising fluid, following the manufacturer's instructions – having removed the nappy liner and contents, which can be flushed down the loo.

## Keeping things clean – disposables

Use the reseal tabs to wrap the disposable nappy, then tie it up in a plastic bag.

Disposables are extremely convenient and are being improved for dryness all the time. Once you've sorted out a good size and make, buy in bulk. You will get through them very quickly (probably using six to ten a day in the early weeks). The cost mounts up, but there are no extras to buy.

Always wash your hands after changing nappies (whichever type) to keep those bugs at bay. Important: be extra careful after LT has had his polio jabs at two, three, four and eighteen months, as the live virus will be in his stools for about a month.

*Happy crappy nappy changing!*

*Buy disposables in bulk*

55

# TAKING LT OUT

Right... so you've been home for a bit, that's going quite well and you've decided it's time for your first outing. This might be a few days after his birth, or it could be a couple of weeks, whenever you feel ready.

Taking LT out is great. You get some exercise and a change of scenery, LT gets some fresh air and lots of strangers go starry-eyed over your baby. If you feel anxious about getting everything ready, take your partner or a friend with you for the first few trips. Take it easy at first. Just go to the shops, or perhaps the baby clinic, where you can see your health visitor or GP and meet other new parents.

## How will he travel?

Horizontal is best. If he's in a pushchair, make sure he can lie flat. It's too soon for his back to be propped up. A pram is ideal, but many parents don't have enough room for one. Slings are great. He usually stays snug and happy. The only problem might be loading and unloading. Not too bad, initially, but a bit awkward when he gets heavier. If he's going in the car, the law requires a properly secured, backward-facing baby seat, or a carry-cot with special straps.

## How much should he wear?

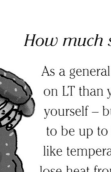

As a general rule, put a little more on LT than you are wearing yourself – but don't think he has to be up to the hospital's sauna-like temperatures. Babies quickly lose heat from their heads so, in cold weather, he'll need a hat to keep the warmth in. Keeping him at a constant temperature is best so, when taking him from a centrally heated house to the car wrap him up well. If it's warm in the car, take his wrappings off, otherwise he'll overheat.

### Sunshine
LT's skin will burn very easily so, in hot weather, use a sun block cream and protect him with a sun hat and light clothing. If taking him out in the pram or pushchair, use a canopy.

# HEALTH AND SAFETY

Worrying about your new baby's well-being is completely natural. Everyone does it. Here are a few worries and hazards, and tips on how to deal with them.

## *Worries/Hazards survival tips*

🎀 **Fontanelles** These are the two soft spots on LT's head. The back fontanelle closes at about six weeks, the front scalp bones don't join together until LT is eighteen months old. These spots are tougher than you think as they are protected by a strong membrane. You can wash them when you wash LT's hair.

🐾 **Toddlers and animals** Don't leave him alone at any time with either.

🐾 **Worried about his health or development?** See your health visitor or GP – that's what they are there for.

🐾 **Bugs, sickness, diarrhoea** Wash your hands after changing nappies. Sterilise all feeding equipment.

🦟 **Cot death** Always put LT to sleep on his back. Avoid overheating with too many bedclothes or over-wrapping. Place LT's feet at the end of the cot, with covers up to his chest, so he can't wriggle down under them and become too hot. Avoid smoking in the same room as LT.

🦟 **Safety** Keep a smoke alarm and fire extinguisher in the house.

🦟 **Scalds and burns** Put the affected area under the cold tap or in a bowl of cool water for ten minutes, then wrap the area in a clean, non-fluffy cloth, such as a cotton pillow case or tea towel, or in cling film, to avoid infection. Go to hospital or call your GP.

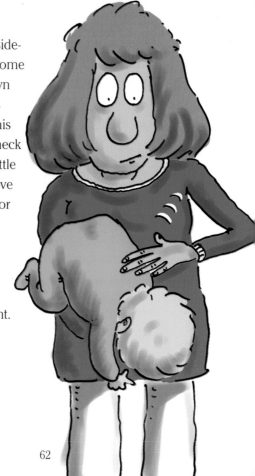

**Choking** Hold LT upside-down to help the object come out, then lie him face down over your knee and hit his back firmly. Gently open his mouth, look inside and check for any object with your little finger. If attempts to remove it are unsuccessful, send for an ambulance.

**Heat rash** *(tiny red spots mostly on face)* Fewer layers of clothing – rash goes without treatment.

62

**Milk spots** *(common after first 2 weeks)* Distressing and LT won't look at his best. Usually goes without treatment; if not, see GP.

**Snuffly nose** *(Can't breathe easily when feeding or asleep)* Nose drops, or capsules containing decongestant (not menthol) on a cloth at night.

There are obviously plenty of other potential hazards, but they are more likely to affect babies over six weeks old. If your local mothers' or Red Cross group runs a baby resuscitation course, it's worth attending. Your health visitor should have details.

## *So that's about it*

There is a certain amount you can do to get ready for your Little Terror's arrival but, as you've probably already discovered, nothing can really prepare you for the experience, and you just have to take every day as it comes.

Like everything else in life, some people are naturals, others have mixed feelings and have to work at it. The one sure thing is that every effort you make is rewarded somewhere along the line. Good or bad, it's important to share your feelings with each other, or with a friend. To look after LT, you need to look after yourself and each other. If at first it seems tough going, remember that being a parent can be the most fulfilling experience of your life.